THE WITCH OF PORT LAJOYE

Joyce Barkhouse

Illustrated by Daphne Irving

Ragweed Press
Charlottetown, 1983

This book
is dedicated to
Lorenda

The author wishes to thank Doreen Sark and Gillian
Robinson who helped research the other versions
of this legend.

Ragweed Press
Box 2023, Charlottetown
Prince Edward Island, C1A 7N7

Canadian Cataloguing in Publication Data

Barkhouse, Joyce, 1913-

The witch of Port LaJoye

ISBN 0-920304-26-5

1. Micmac Indians - Folklore.   2. Indians of North
America - Prince Edward Island.   3. Legends - Prince
Edward Island.   I. Irving, Daphne, 1931-
II. Title.

PS8553.A87 1983   398.2'089970717   C83-099055-0
PZ8.1.B37Wi 1983

Prologue

In the great oral literature of the primitive tribes of North America, the tales of the Wabanaki Indians of the east coast are unique. Ever since the Rev. Silas T. Rand and Charles Leland—scholars of the early nineteenth century—transcribed and translated the legends of the Micmac, students of mythology have tried their hands at re-shaping and re-telling these ancient myths.

In her foreword to *Glooscap and His Magic*, Kay Hill says:

> In general, the supernatural heroes of the North American appear as tricksters with contradictory qualities of wisdom and stupidity, of goodness and malice. Only Glooscap of the Wabanaki appears continually as benefactor and friend. Perhaps for this reason the Legends of the Wabanaki are in spirit and meaning unlike anything else in the mythology of North America.

The Micmac were nomads, who wandered all over Nova Scotia, up the northeast coast of New Brunswick to the Gaspé, across to Prince Edward Island, sometimes venturing as far as Newfoundland. Through the ages many strange tales were told around remote wilderness campfires, stories of the creation of the earth, the sun, the moon and the stars; of plants and animals; of stones and islands; of winds and floods; stories of the supernatural and of the peculiar behaviour of certain human beings. These stories were passed down from generation to generation and so they came to vary greatly in the telling. Who can say which is original?

After the arrival of the white man, storytellers interwove new themes which described something of the impact of the intruders upon the social life of the Indians.

Many Versions of "La Belle Marie"

The legend of "La Belle Marie" is still part of the oral tradition of the Micmac, and there are at least ten written versions of the story. In several accounts, Marie, the daughter of a Basque woman, marries the son of a Micmac chief and lives happily ever after. In another account, Marie is shot and killed with the arrow of a Micmac angered that the chief's son would marry a paleface. In yet another version, Marie steps into the

3

path of an arrow intended for her new husband and dies in his arms.

One version of the story sent chills down our spines and raised a question. This account is based on a manuscript found by Frank Deedmeyer attached inside a copy of an old Micmac Prayer Book, in which a young girl named Marie was brought to trial, condemned, and executed for witchcraft. The burning took place on November 17, 1723, at Point de la Flame. Might a girl of 17 actually have been burned at the stake at Port LaJoye?

Burned at the Stake

On September 4, 1909, an old Micmac Indian named Sosep entered the office of Frank Deedmeyer, the American Consul to Charlottetown, Prince Edward Island. Sosep had with him an old book, the ragged, yellowed pages of which were covered with hieroglyphs, with superscriptions in German. It was a Roman Catholic prayer book in the Micmac language.

Fastened inside the heavy cover was a manuscript in French on thin paper, written in so fine a hand and so faint that many portions could be deciphered only with the aid of a magnifying glass.

The account told of the burning at the stake of a witch known as "La Belle Marie" in 1723 at Port LaJoye. Port LaJoye was the garrison town at the mouth of the Hillsborough River, the site of present-day Fort Amherst, a short distance from Charlottetown.

The story was written by a French missionary and addressed to "my beloved Brother Ambrose, disciple of Saint Francis, now a missionary priest among the Micmac savages on the Isle of St. Jean, North America." According to the records at the Louisbourg Archives in Nova Scotia, this Brother Ambrose was probably Ambroise Aubré, Recollet missionary to Port LaJoye from 1739 to 1741 and from 1751 to 1754.

Frank Deedmeyer's curiosity was so excited by what he read that he spent many months bargaining with Sosep for possession of the Micmac Prayer Book, which he finally obtained, along with two battle axes.

After making a translation of the manuscript, Deedmeyer sent the Prayer Book and axes to the Smithsonian Institution in Washington, D.C.

Adhering closely to this account, Joyce Barkhouse has re-
told the story for children in *The Witch of Port LaJoye.*

The Basques

Marie's mother, according to the Deedmeyer translation,
was a Basque from Bayonne. The Basques, who have often
been called the "mystery people of Europe," were regarded as
barbarians because as late as the eleventh century they had
not yet adopted Christianity. The Basques are often described
as proud, inscrutable, and freedom-loving people. Perhaps
above all, the Basques are known for their singing.

> Hope rises from their hearts to their lips like a song from
> heaven. That is why the Basques are always singing. Basque
> songs, as old as those which the wind sings to the oaks of
> Aralar, have been heard even in the concentration camps of the
> Sahara. But even the prison guards were touched by these
> songs, and they let many escape and sail for America.
>
> Basques continue to sing even when they are marching to their
> death. A young man who had succeeded in escaping from
> Franco's Spain into France told me the following story: One
> morning in an old house near the cemetery where he had taken
> refuge, he was awakened by a magnificent chorus of young
> voices singing the Basque Hymn of the Gudaris. Convinced
> that this was a hymn of victory, he rushed out of his hiding-
> place to greet the singers. He was hastily pulled back by his
> protector, who told him that it was a wagon-load of Basque
> prisoners going to their execution. "We often hear that song at
> daybreak," he said. They listened to the stirring chorus as it
> died away in the distance. Then came the sound of shots, and
> the singing and the singers were stilled forever.*

In this story of *The Witch of Port LaJoye,* La Belle Marie
sings from her prison cell and sings as she is burned at the
stake.

---

*From *Freedom Was Flesh and Blood* by José Antonio de Aguirre.
London, Victor Gollancz Ltd, 1945.

The Mystery of the Missing Manuscript

Anxious to see the original manuscript attached inside the Prayer Book, we wrote to the Smithsonian Institution. The Smithsonian reported that it could find in its records no reference either to the Deedmeyer translation or to the Micmac Prayer Book. Alarmed, we wrote again, sending copies of the letters which Frank Deedmeyer had written to accompany the Prayer Book and battle axes when he shipped them off to Washington, D.C. in 1910. We enclosed copies of letters sent back to Deedmeyer by the Smithsonian, acknowledging receipt of the Prayer Book and axes. We also sent along a copy of a letter which had been written in February of 1980 by a museum specialist with the Department of Anthropology at the Smithsonian saying that the Smithsonian had the "Deedmeyer" Prayer Book as well as parts of three other Micmac Prayer Books.

We heard again from the Smithsonian. A copy of the Micmac Prayer Book had been found, but there was no attached account "in French or any other language" inside the front cover.

The mystery surrounding the disappearance of this manuscript has a precedent. The edition of the Micmac Prayer Book to which was attached the account of La Belle Marie was published in Vienna, Austria, in 1866 by Reverend Christian Kauder. It was then the only book ever printed in the hieroglyphic of the Micmac and had over 5703 types specially cut and cast for it. Earlier Micmac prayer books were laboriously copied by hand. The Kauder book was ill-fated. Most copies were destroyed in a shipwreck. Only the first shipment of the 1866 Kauder edition ever reached America.

Bubbling Springs

There are a number of bubbling springs on Prince Edward Island which are said to be the spring which held the sacred healing stone of Mineota and said to be the spring near which Marie and her mother camped. In the Deedmeyer manuscript and in subsequent versions of the legend, these magical sources are described in words uncannily similar to those of the poet Longfellow in his poem "Evangeline." In the preface to a facsimile reprint of the 1866 Kauder edition, there is a note that a copy of the Prayer Book was sent to Longfellow.

6

Perhaps the Deedmeyer manuscript and translation were a clever literary joke. The winters on Prince Edward Island are long and hard. Deedmeyer may have decided to have some fun writing an imaginary account, using enough historical fact to make his romantic story of Marie appear true.

We are still on the lookout for the missing manuscript. It may well be in the Smithsonian. Or it may be discovered that Frank Deedmeyer has been having a good story on several generations of us. Whatever the "real" story is, *The Witch of Port LaJoye* is a spellbinding and haunting tale. Joyce Barkhouse has set the spirits of Mineota and La Belle Marie singing again.

Deirdre Kessler,
Charlottetown,
Prince Edward Island.

1

The Stone of Mineota

Long ago, when the great god Glooscap watched over his Indian people on the island of Abegweit, a grieving Micmac chief whose name was Kiotsaton, wandered away from the rest of his tribe. He had with him his young son and daughter. The boy's name was Kitpou, and the girl was called Mineota.

Deep in a forest they came upon a small lake fed by a clear, bubbling spring. Here, where towering pines and bearded spruces protected the shimmering water on every side, Kiotsaton made camp.

On the third night, when the children were asleep in the wigwam and a new moon sailed like a bright canoe across the midnight sky, Kiotsaton sat brooding, cross-legged, beside his dying fire. Suddenly he realized he was not alone. Another man sat beside him.

"Kwa!" said the stranger, in Micmac greeting.

"Kwa!" replied Kiotsaton, not at all pleased to know that someone had discovered his peaceful retreat. "Who are you, and what do you want?"

"I am Glooscap," replied the stranger, in a deep and echoing voice. "Move away from this dread spot, or great harm will befall you."

Kiotsaton leaped to his feet. Red light from the fire flickered on the noble features of the stranger, and Kiotsaton knew then that it was Glooscap.

Greatly astonished, he stammered, "Why, what harm can befall me in this sweet place?"

Glooscap looked at him sternly.

"An angry spirit inhabits the spring which lies before you. If you venture upon these waters, called Minnewauken, the Evil One will grow violent and your life will be in danger."

Kiotsaton was silent. He looked long upon the moonlit surface of the lake which reflected the black shadows of the forest. Then he sighed.

"My heart has been tormented with grief for my dead wife. Only here have I found comfort and peace. Here I must stay until my spirit heals."

Glooscap rose to his feet. And as Kiotsaton watched, the god grew taller and taller until he towered far above him, higher than any tree in the forest. His voice rumbled like distant thunder.

"You have been warned. Make sure that you or your children never enter the lake called Minnewauken."

Glooscap seemed to dissolve into a white mist, which floated away above the dark forest.

In the morning Kiotsaton told his children what Glooscap had said.

"All the same, we can fish in the fine stream that flows into Minnewauken. As long as we do not venture upon the waters of the lake itself, we will be safe here," he explained.

And so Kiotsaton the chief stayed, and his children grew up beside beautiful lake Minnewauken. They never forgot Glooscap's warning, and never put a canoe or even a fish-net into the water.

All went well, until at last one day in early autumn, when her father and brother had gone hunting, the fair Mineota went berry-picking along the shore. She came to a place where branches of luscious red fruit hung over the water's edge. As she leaned over to pick the berries, she looked down and saw her own reflection in the still water.

"Oh! I am beautiful!" she exclaimed.

Enraptured, she knelt down to look more closely, but as she did so her long hair touched the water. Instantly there came a deep gurgling sound and a whirlpool formed and widened. Mineota moved back just in time to avoid being sucked down into the whirlpool. Her heart pounded with fright as she glimpsed the green, slimy back of a monster, undulating like a serpent in the middle of the lake.

That night Mineota told her brother what had happened. But Kitpou hardly listened. That day he had killed his first caribou, and he was bursting with pride in his accomplishment.

"I am now a man, a great hunter," he told Mineota, strutting back and forth before her. "If the monster were to show himself, he would show himself to me, not to a mere girl. You must have seen ripples and shadows of clouds moving across the water."

Mineota was troubled, but she said no more about it.

One day Kiotsaton had the misfortune to step into a hole and twist his ankle. He limped home painfully, unable to hunt anymore.

"Never mind," said Kitpou. "I'll keep the cooking pot filled." And off he went to hunt by himself. But luck was not with him. After several days he returned to the far shore of Minnewauken, carrying his canoe upon his weary shoulders. Across the water he could see his father and sister broiling trout over the campfire. He was tired and hungry. What a short distance it was across the lake, and what a long way around!

"How silly to be afraid! The lake is as calm as a beaver pond," he thought.

Quickly he launched his canoe. Nothing happened until he had paddled half way across, then suddenly he heard strange noises coming from the direction of the spring. The water beneath him began to churn and bubble. Waves grew higher and higher and broke in thunderous foam. The canoe was tossed about like a dry leaf. Then a long green arm slid out of the water, wrapped itself around the canoe and drew it down into the raging whirlpool.

From the shore Kiotsaton and his daughter watched in helpless horror. In a few moments the lake subsided and was as peaceful as before, but Kitpou was gone forever.

That night Kiotsaton went down alone to the bubbling spring and threw rocks into the water, calling out in rage and grief, "Come forth, Evil One, and show yourself!"

The waters of Minnewauken began to froth and boil and for a moment the serpent's back was exposed. Instantly the chief fitted an arrow to his bow and a moment later, when the monster reared its ugly head, he let fly. With a hiss and a snarl the head disappeared, but now began such a commotion as had never been seen or heard before in all the island of Abegweit. The waters of the spring rose and towered up into the sky, then fell in a roaring flood, which began to rush up over the land.

"Mineota! Mineota!" Kiotsaton cried to his daughter. As she emerged from the wigwam, he seized her hand. Together they fled through the forest.

"We must climb the hill!" gasped Kiotsaton, and they ran for their lives. But even as they threw themselves, exhausted, at the top, the waters arose all around them.

And then, above the tumult, came the thundering voice of Glooscap.

"See what damage you have done! Now the flood will rise and cover all the island. All my people will be drowned."

Kiotsaton lifted his clasped hands in prayer.

"You have been warned," said Glooscap, and he seemed to dissolve into a white mist.

"Help us! What can we do?" he cried.

And the terrible voice of Glooscap replied, "The spirit of Minnewauken must be appeased. You must give your daughter as a sacrifice."

"Never!" cried Kiotsaton.

"Then all must die," said Glooscap, and his presence faded from above the forest.

But Mineota heard his words. Silently she slipped from her father's grasp and disappeared into the troubled waters below. The offended spirit was appeased. The waters returned to their natural level and all was as calm as before.

Kiotsaton was alone on the hilltop. For a long time he lay as one dead. Then Glooscap appeared before him.

"Your daughter's sacrifice shall not go unrewarded," he said. "The spirit of the fair Mineota shall return and live on within a stone which you will find where your wigwam stood. This stone shall have healing powers for the people of your tribe alone. It is for you, Kiotsatan, to use all the days of your life, but when you die it must be dropped into the deep bubbling spring of Minnewauken."

"And after my death, may the medicine stone never be used again?" asked Kiotsaton sadly.

"If the one who enters the waters of Minnewauken to seek it thinks only of the one to be healed, and has no thought of self, then the stone can be brought out and used again to heal those of Micmac blood."

"And how can this stone be distinguished from any other?" Kiosaton persisted.

"The stone of Mineota cannot be mistaken. It will be of bright copper colour and shaped like a cone," said Glooscap, and he faded from the chief's sight.

And so Kiotsaton returned to the scene of his horrible misfortune. There he found the healing stone. He built a wigwam near the place of the old one and became a noted medicine man of his race. Many were the cures he wrought with the famous medicine stone, which held the spirit of the fair Mineota. Shortly before his death, Chief Kiotsaton dropped it into the deepest part of the spring. There the sacred stone lay hidden.

2

La Belle Marie

For hundreds of years the medicine stone lay at the bottom of the spring. It was not forgotten, because the story lived on among the Indians, but no one had the courage to recover it by diving into the dangerous waters.

At last the time came when the Micmac of Abegweit began to share their island with the French people, who came out of the ocean in their great winged canoes. In the year of our Lord 1720 they built a small fort at a place they called Port LaJoye and they did not leave when winter came, as all European fishermen had done before.

They called the island Isle St. Jean and they made it their permanent home. A village of small huts grew up around the fort, and from this base the Bretons and the Basques and the Acadian settlers travelled the waterways to explore the island.

Some settled on the north shore in a favourable spot now called St. Peter's. Not far from this settlement was the spring-fed lake which the Indians called Minnewauken, but which the French named La Grande Source.

Of course, the settlers knew nothing about the evil spirit which inhabited the water until the Indians tried to warn them, and then they only laughed. Indeed the spirit seemed to have no power over the aliens, who ventured upon the lake without harm. Perhaps the stone might have stayed forever in the depths of the dark pool and no terrible mischief been done if it had not been for the sudden appearance of Madame Grandville and her daughter, two years after the settlement had been established.

Now up until this time the canoe-shaped island lay cradled on the waves of the North Atlantic, undisturbed by civilization. Each spring great flocks of wildfowl came to nest in reedy marshes and herds of sea-cows and seals came to the wide sandy beaches to have their babies on ice floes or among the rolling dunes. Thick primeval forest covered the land, and through shadowy branches fierce pine martens hunted squirrels and robbed song-birds of their eggs. Beneath the huge evergreens bears and wolves had their lairs and many hundreds of smaller creatures of the northern forest lived out the pattern of their lives.

Each spring, many of the Micmac Indians came from the mainland to camp and to enjoy the eggs of the waterfowl, the sweet wild berries, and the fat fish which came up the rivers to spawn. But some of them, before the first snow fell, got into their canoes and paddled back to the mainland, for there were no moose and no beaver on the island, and these were their staples for winter food.

The French stayed all through the long and lonely winters when the narrow strait which separated the island from Acadia was jammed with ice floes and no ship could enter the frozen harbour. Even in summer few visitors called at this lonely outpost; and that was why the sudden appearance of the two women was so mysterious. For they came in the night and no person ever saw the ship which brought them.

By the spring of 1721 the construction of the fort at Port LaJoye was almost completed. It was a large, square fortification with eighteen cannons mounted, and sturdy barracks surrounded by a broad, deep ditch. A deep, vaulted gunpowder storehouse ran from the end of the barracks to a point on the shore just above the high water mark, with an entrance between two rocks. An underground prison connected with the powder magazine.

Most of the settlers had remained at Port LaJoye, but several families, hearing of a shipyard established on the north shore, had abandoned their rude cabins to go to St. Peter's where the men could enjoy the security of regular employment. It was in one of these deserted huts of Port LaJoye that Madame Grandville and her daughter first took up their abode. Soon the fishermen's wives were busy speculating as to who these strange women were and why they had come to Port LaJoye.

Madame Grandville was a woman of commanding, almost masculine appearance. Her intimidating manner forbade too many questions. She confessed only that she was a Basque from Bayonne, and that she had been the first white woman to settle in Bienville, on the Gulf of Mexico. There she had lived with the Indians until she had met and married an English sea merchant, Captain John Grandville, and she had travelled with him to far places. Her daughter Marie had been born in 1705 in Hispaniola and there, on a beautiful estate, the little family had lived happily until Marie was fifteen years old. That year, said Madame, her husband had set sail for South America and had never returned. Finally word had come that his ship had been wrecked at the mouth of the Orinoco River and all on board had perished. And that was why, she explained, she had come north on board a merchantman bound for Port Royal in Acadia, seeking to join her brother. But when she arrived she was told that he had removed to Isle St. Jean, so Madame had persuaded the merchantman's captain to take her to Port LaJoye. He had arrived at night, dropped anchor long enough to put her and Marie ashore, and then taken advantage of favourable winds to continue up the Gulf of St. Lawrence to Quebec.

"And what is the name of your brother?" she was asked, but when she gave it no one had heard of such a person.

Madame only shrugged. "I must have been misinformed. He must have been stationed elsewhere," she said. But she never suggested that she would proceed any farther with her search.

As for Marie, if anyone tried to question her, she only tossed her head and laughed. She was interested in the present, not in the past. High-spirited and carefree, she was by far the most beautiful girl on the island.

Marie and her mother travelled about freely and soon were accepted by both the French and Indians. Sometimes they visited for a week in the home of a fisherman. The Basques, especially, were delighted with their company, for Madame was from their homeland. She spoke their language and understood their customs. As for Marie, she could dance like a fairy and sing like a bird. As soon as a fiddler took up his violin the girl was on her feet, whirling and dipping in her colourful gowns, as light and pretty as a butterfly. She performed many exotic steps of her own, stamping her feet and snapping her fingers in time to the music.

Equally at home with the Indians, Madame and her daughter often appeared at an encampment to join in a feast or a session of story-telling. Marie adopted the dances of the Micmac, bowing and shuffling faster and faster to the hypnotic beat of the drums. Soon she was known all over Isle St. Jean. They called her "La Belle Marie." She smiled and was friendly with them all, but gave her favours to none.

The first year passed pleasantly. When winter came

19

and many of the Indians returned to the mainland, Madame Grandville and Marie moved north to St. Peter's. There the French carpenters helped them build a comfortable cabin at Minnewauken, where Kiotsaton had lived out his days as a great healer long, long before.

All winter the settlers and the Indians who remained on the Island worked and relaxed together. When the men were not away hunting, they occupied themselves with the manufacture of oars and paddles, the mending of nets or the framing of snowshoes. The Indian women stitched and embroidered leather garments, while the Frenchwomen worked to the whirr of spinning wheels and the clicking of wooden knitting needles. Sometimes all work was put aside for an evening of music and dancing and story-telling, and then La Belle Marie, with her enchanting voice and graceful figure, was a desired guest, a welcome addition to every party.

Unfortunately, this happy state of affairs could not last. It was inevitable that Marie should become the envy of more than one young maiden and her mother, and these jealous women began to whisper among themselves.

"Where does Madame Grandville get all her money?" someone asked. "It seems that whenever a supply ship comes into port, she can buy anything that suits her fancy."

And another said, "She must have buried treasure. Every once in a while she sneaks off into the forest and comes back with a pouch filled with gold and silver."

It was agreed, in any case, that she could not have come by such riches honestly. It was incredible that the Grandvilles should have so much, when everyone else had to live in the most primitive manner, and get by with the barest necessities. Before long wild rumours were told as truth.

Madame practised medicine. She had strange, exotic

...a hand appeared above the surface of the water, passing to her a bag....

herbs and roots and other ingredients which she had brought with her from the West Indies. With these she mixed salves and brewed potions. Now, instead of being grateful for her treatments, the jealous women began to whisper that Madame was a witch! At least they knew something about how to protect themselves from her evil powers. Witches always feared red. So, they made little crosses of twigs of the rowan tree, whose berries are red. They believed that the blood of Christ had fallen on a rowan tree as he hung on the cross. Some mothers tied bits of red yarn into the hair of their children.

Before the next summer was over the women began to complain to the priests. These were two Sulpician monks, Father De Breslay and the Reverend Marie Anselme de Meticier, the first priests ever to set foot upon the island. They had arrived at almost the same time as the Grandvilles, and they were dedicated, as they said, "to the saving of the souls of heathen Indians." For old, arthritic Father De Breslay, every soul won for Catholicism was a step towards Heaven, and each soul lost was a step towards Hell. Now he was greatly alarmed as he listened to the accusations of the women. They said they had it on good authority that the so-called Captain Grandville had not been an honest sea merchant, but an infamous buccaneer.

"He was not drowned off the coast of South America," shrilled one. "His pirate ship was captured and he was taken to England. A sailor told me that he saw the criminal Grandville hanged on the dock at London."

"And Madame Grandville used to sail with him," added another. "She herself has admitted that. Now we know that she was his accomplice. She has a price on her own head. That explains why she and her daughter are hiding out here at this lonely outpost."

As for Marie, they said she was no better than her mother.

"Her father was a Protestant, a heretic. Haven't you noticed that Marie seldom accompanies her mother to mass, and never to confession?"

"Whenever Madame and Marie visit an Indian encampment," they said viciously, "the Roman Catholic members of the tribe revert to their old beliefs. We have seen Marie participate openly in their dances and tribal rites."

Father De Breslay spent the night in prayer. Perhaps he had ignored for too long the "saving of heathen souls." He had felt it necessary to erect a church where the people of Port LaJoye could come to worship. He was proud of the small edifice built on a headland at the entrance to the harbour. Behind it, on the highest summit, stood a tall black cross to proclaim to all navigators that Isle St. Jean was a Christian land.

Now it seemed to the dedicated monk that the Devil, in the persons of two evil women, had dogged his footsteps and would undo all his good works unless strong measures were taken. He began to preach against the women on Sundays. Weekdays, he and Father Anselem went from house to house, warning and admonishing the settlers to have nothing more to do with La Belle Marie and her mother.

As the French were taught to avoid the women, more and more weird tales were whispered about them. The women did not trust their men to stay away from the Grandvilles. In fact, when a man was accused of having been seen coming out of the Basque woman's hut he admitted he had gone to buy favourable winds from the old witch. He showed them the charm he had bought—a string of nine knots. When he was at sea, each time he wanted to make the wind veer to avert a storm, he could untie a knot. He said that the old Basque woman had wonderful medicines, too—medicines that could deaden the pain of a toothache or heal a festering sore. For a man in pain, it was hard to stay away.

As for all that ready money, an explanation was soon forthcoming. One belated traveller, passing La Grande Source after midnight, saw Madame Grandville slowly rising from the depths of the pool. And when she set foot on the bank a hand appeared above the surface of the water, passing to her a bag, the contents of which jingled like coins as it was deposited on the ground.

Different tales were told about La Belle Marie. Often she was heard singing strange songs with unknown words in Basque as she went about her household tasks. She sang, too, as she wandered in the forest. So sweet was her voice and so haunting the melodies it was impossible not to stop to listen. La Belle Marie was an enchantress. Her magic was in her smile and infectious laughter, in the compelling glance of her dark, luminous eyes and in her singing. Above all, there was magic in her singing.

When Marie and her mother found they were no longer welcome at the fort or in the homes of the fishermen and nobody came to visit them, they began to spend more and more time in the company of the Micmac.

Marie loved the wilderness and adapted easily to the Indian way of life. She discarded her long skirts in favour of a knee length shift of soft leather, and her red shoes for embroidered moccasins. When the women went to gather berries she went with them and watched how fruit was boiled, shaped into cakes and dried in the sun for winter use. Egg yolks, too, were boiled hard, dried, powdered and packed into little skin pouches. But Marie grew impatient with much of the work of the women. She preferred to go hunting with the men rather than stay at home to prepare meat, stitch leggings or embroider peaked caps with dyed porcupine quills. Strong and graceful, quick of hand and keen of eye, soon

24

Marie could paddle a canoe and use a bow and arrow as skilfully as any brave.

Before summer was over it was known that La Belle Marie had fallen in love with an Indian and he with her. His name was Kaktoogwassees, the Young Thunderer. Marie found favour with the young man's father, chief of the tribe. Late that autumn at the *uik paltimk*, or farewell feast, celebrated before the withdrawal of most of the hunters to the mainland, the chief announced the betrothal of his son to the beautiful paleface.

At this announcement an ugly murmur arose among the braves. They had applauded La Belle Marie's singing and dancing. They had admired her intelligence and skill and the ease with which she had fitted into their way of life, but they would not accept a paleface as a wife of one who should become a leader of the Micmac.

It was the custom when non-Micmac women were captured in raids to use them as slaves, to help the women with work. Although La Belle Marie was not a captive, and had achieved a special status within the tribe, she was still an alien. It was unthinkable that she should marry Kaktoogwassees.

As the sounds of protest grew louder at the *uik paltimk*, one voice was raised above the others. The oldest sagamore strode forward to confront Kaktoogwassees.

"You have insulted my daughter! Only six months ago you painted your face red, came to my wigwam and asked to enter. I greeted you and asked you to come into the back part of the wigwam, the place of warmth and honour, to sit beside me. You gave my daughter, Nessowa, a gift of a fine bearskin. This she accepted, and in return she made you moccasins, beautifully embroidered, and corded your snowshoes. These gifts you accepted, so it was understood that you would live in my wigwam this winter and in the spring you would marry my daughter. Everyone knows this. Do you dare to break your promise?"

Kaktoogwassees turned pale, but as he stood up to face his accuser his father stepped forward to answer for him.

"It is true that your daughter found favour with my son before the arrival of La Belle Marie. It is true that he and Nessowa have exchanged gifts but, as everyone knows, a betrothal is not complete until a man has lived nine moons in the father-in-law's wigwam. This Kaktoogwassees has not done. Therefore he is free to marry the girl of his choice."

At this the sagamore snatched up his hatchet and shook it threateningly. Instantly a dozen other braves stood and followed his example. "Hau! Hau! Hau!" they shouted in agreement. But Kaktoogwassees and his father stood steadfast, arms folded, while some of the women clustered protectively around La Belle Marie.

With a last vow of vengeance, the sagamore led his family and followers away from the *uik paltimk*.

That winter La Belle Marie and her mother stayed in the wigwam of Kaktoogwassees and his family. Marie slept beside her mother on the opposite side of the central fire from her betrothed, as was the custom.

During this time it was traditional for the betrothed girl to make her future husband's clothes, cord his snowshoes, and show in every way possible that she would make a good wife. Marie was not clever with her needle. She had been petted and spoiled in her childhood and had had slaves to sew for her. She tried to learn, and the women liked her all the better because her stitches were clumsier than theirs.

Marie had other talents. In the summer Micmac women made bright dyes of red and blue and violet from the roots of certain plants and the bark of certain trees. When the women painted designs on soft mooseskin with these bright colours, Marie created astonishing new pictures of flowers and leaves and birds, such as the Micmac had never seen before. She made two hair-strings of unusual design for Kaktoogwassees of dyed porcupine quills and bits of clam shells, and they glittered and sparkled with gold and jewels given to her by her mother. Kaktoogwassees wore them proudly.

Marie now always dressed like an Indian maiden, in a knee-length leather robe girdled tightly at the waist, with separate sleeves and long, fringed leggings. She pulled back her long brown hair from her face and tied it behind with a leather cord. Her mother did likewise.

Madame Grandville was getting old and somewhat stiff. Her face was wrinkled and tired. The only important thing in her life now was the happiness of her daughter. She herself was content to stay at home to help the other women, but Marie, whenever she could, went out hunting with the men. Although it was against tradition, the braves made no objections. Indeed, they soon said that she brought them good luck. That winter there was always food in the cooking pot.

Most important of any hunt was the quest for moose. Marie learned how to look for broken tips of branches to show where moose had browsed, and she learned to discern by the taste of a broken twig how recently an animal had been nibbling. She learned how to stalk on snowshoes, and when a great lordly beast had been sighted, she knelt beside Kaktoogwassees in the snow and heard him whisper, "Turn your eyes the other way, my Brother, for we have need of you. We need your meat to keep us from starvation and we need your skin to keep us from freezing." When La Belle Marie drew her bow, her arrow went as straight and true to the mark as that of Kaktoogwassees.

Often it was Marie who tramped swiftly back to camp to tell the women where the moose had fallen, for an Indian hunter never carried home the meat of his kill.

While Marie went to fetch the women, the men cut out the tongue, heart, kidneys, and entrails of the fallen animal. They took these delicacies home to feast upon while the women and girls went off, singing with joy, to finish the job of butchering. Then there was a great feast. The successful hunters took the smallest shares of all. It was their great pleasure to serve the meat, the result of their prowess, to others. When the men had eaten their fill the women and children gathered around to enjoy what was left.

After a feast it was often time for storytelling. Sometimes Marie and her mother would sit with the women for long evenings around the fire, while the chief or one of the braves told marvellous tales of sorcery and magic; of *boowins* who could change themselves into the forms of animals. They listened to stories of the stars in the heavens, and of spirits that lived in deep springs that bubbled out of the earth to form pools and lakes.

So it was that Marie first learned of the legend of the fair Mineota. She heard how the beautiful Indian girl had given her life to save her people by stopping the great flood. She heard how the god Glooscap commanded Mineota's spirit to enter a healing stone which now lay at the bottom of a spring near Lake Minnewauken.

Madame Grandville and Marie were surprised to learn that this was none other than La Grande Source. Marie had often bathed in the pool and had gone out in a canoe upon the surface of the lake. No harm had come to her. But when Indians heard this they laughed softly, and explained that she was a paleface. The evil spirit knew that the stone was be used to cure only those of the Micmac tribe, and so it was not troubled by her presence.

Sometimes Marie became a storyteller. She had a way with children, and often they gathered around her saying, "Tell us of faraway lands. Sing us a song." Marie

Into the magic circle they placed all their colourful ornaments.

would sing of her life in the far South, where there was never any snow or ice; where bright, vivid flowers bloomed in all seasons; where the warm ocean was the colour of a bluejay's wing; and where delicious, funny flying fish obligingly jumped out of the water into the boats of the fishermen. Marie sang of golden fruit that grew on trees, fruit as much bigger than the tiny wild berries of the north as a bear is bigger than a mouse. The children laughed, and beat with short sticks upon rolls of bark to keep time to her singing.

If a baby cried Marie was first to pick up the cradle-board and unwrap the little blanket of feathered goose-skin and change the soft moss that served as a diaper. She cuddled the infant in her arms and crooned a lullaby she had composed in Micmac words. Sometimes she caught the eye of Kaktoogwassees watching her. He would smile, and La Belle Marie would drop her long eyelashes and blush because she knew he too was thinking of the day she would cradle their own baby in her arms.

So the winter passed and the days grew longer and warmer. In the woodlands the snow melted. The first flower of spring, the rosy-lipped, honey-hearted arbutus, opened its pale pink waxy blossoms to breathe sweet fragrance upon the air. This was the signal to the women to take down the wigwams, pack the canoes and get ready to return to their summer homes along the shores of Abegweit.

All winter nothing had been seen of the angry sagamore, father of Nessowa, or his family and followers. A rumour was heard that they had travelled far up into the Gaspé, and were not likely to return to Abegweit. All the same Kaktoogwassees warned Marie that they must always be on the lookout, because the sagamore had sworn vengeance and would never forgive an insult to his proud family.

Marie shivered and was afraid. "Can nothing be done to appease his anger?"

Kaktoogwassees frowned. "Perhaps some lavish gifts, but I have nothing rich enough to offer."

Madame Grandville was listening. She smiled and said, "I have in mind a voyage to the Gulf of Mexico before your wedding day. When we departed in haste from our home in Hispaniola it was impossible to recover all of our buried treasure. I have a dowry for you, my daughter. You shall have a fine gift for Nessowa which will surely protect you from the vengeance of her father."

Marie was delighted.

"I shall go with you, dear Mother!" she exclaimed. "By the time we return, the waiting period of our engagement will be over, and Kaktoogassees and I can be married."

As reluctant as he was to see La Belle Marie go on this long voyage, Kaktoogassees consented, because he felt that her life was in danger until peace had been made with the sagamore.

One morning in May the mother and daughter left the north shore to paddle down the big river to Port LaJoye. There they planned to wait until a West Indian merchantman came into harbour and they could take passage south to the Gulf of Mexico. But fate decreed that they should never reach their destination. The next afternoon their empty canoe was seen drifting out to sea on the tide, as it swept past the fort.

When Kaktoogwassees heard the report he was greatly alarmed. A search party was formed, and the following morning Kaktoogwassees himself came upon the scene of disaster. Not far from Port LaJoye the bodies of the two women lay upon the bank of the river. Madame Grandville was dead. Marie, covered with blood, had suffered many wounds, but she still showed some signs of life. Kaktoogwassees lifted her in his arms and carried her to the nearest wigwam. There, beside himself with grief, he sat cradling the head of the dying girl on his lap.

At last the Medicine Man, Masu, came. He bathed her wounds, blew upon them with his own breath, licked them with his tongue, and then applied an ointment made of red ochre and balsam. Having done what he could of his own knowledge and skill, he went outside and began to chant and beat upon his bark drum, dancing in accompaniment, in an effort to drive away evil spirits that might be waiting to enter the wounds. The people sat cross-legged, watching him with anxious faces. At times Masu stopped and went inside to look at his patient. Marie remained unconscious. As darkness gathered Masu came out for the last time and made a gesture of hopelessness. Then, exhausted, he curled up by the warm embers of the cooking fire. One by one the others slept, but within the wigwam Kaktoogwassees kept watch. He heard the wind sighing through the branches of the great forest and the eerie hunting cry of a nearby owl; then, from far off came the mournful chorus of a pack of wolves.

By morning thick fog enshrouded the island. Masu awakened, and again entered the wigwam to examine the patient. Finally he stood up and placed his hand on the shoulder of Kaktoogwassees.

"Soon her spirit will depart to the Other World," he announced.

He gathered up his medicines and went outside.

Shortly after that the family of Kaktoogwassees came, followed by many other members of the tribe. The women began to weep and chant a mournful dirge but the chief lifted the door-flap of the wigwam and spoke loudly to his son.

"Kaktoogwassees, it is time to fetch the stone of Mineota," he commanded.

Barely had the words left his lips when Masu the Medicine Man and the elders of the tribe leapt forward, protesting loudly.

"No!" said Masu. "It is forbidden that the stone be used to save the life of a paleface. It will lose its healing virtue if used to cure anyone not of Micmac blood."

"Be that as it may!" the chief said. "For a thousand moons no one has dared to defy the evil spirit of Minnewauken. Let my son try!"

There was a murmur of dissent from the braves but the chief overruled all objections. On the next day at high noon Kaktoogwassees, with his father and the Council, arrived at La Grande Source.

His father gave him his blessing and Kaktoogwassees plunged into the chilly waters of the dreaded pool. Down, down he went until his lungs felt as if they were bursting, but even as he touched bottom he saw the gleaming stone of Mineota. In a few moments he rose again to the surface with the sacred stone clutched triumphantly in his hand. Then, with all speed, he hurried back to the wigwam where La Belle Marie lay unconscious.

At first Masu the Medicine Man refused to perform the proper ceremonies, but the chief promised him many fine gifts. At last Masu consented and he received the copper coloured cone reverently and set it upon the ground. Around it he traced a wide circle. He then signalled to the braves, who stepped forward one by one, stripping off their ornaments as they came. Into the magic circle they placed all their colourful bracelets and necklaces and haircords. When all had finished, the women followed their example. Then the children came, with bouquets of white flowers, the fragile blossoms of wild plum and cherry and pear.

Masu led the ceremonial march. Nine times the braves

walked slowly around the stone, heads bowed, calling upon the name of Mineota. Then, at a signal from Masu, Kaktoogwassees entered the wigwam. He brought out the limp form of the dying Marie and laid her within the magic circle. He lifted her right hand and placed it upon the medicine stone. As he watched, praying, he saw her eyelids tremble, her white lips grow red, and a rosy glow appear in her pale cheeks. She opened her eyes and gazed into his with recognition.

Kaktoogwassees' grateful tears fell upon the face of his bethrothed as he carried her back into the wigwam. Almost at once she fell into a healing sleep. The next morning when she awakened she had almost completely recovered.

"Where is my mother?" she asked.

Kaktoogwassees told her of the terrible fate which had overtaken Madame Grandville. He explained that her mother had already been buried.

"She shall be revenged," vowed Kaktoogwassees. "Before our wedding day I shall bring home the hair of Nessowa's father."

But Marie protested passionately. "Nothing can bring back life to my mother. Our enemies are now satisfied. They will leave us in peace. That is all my mother would wish."

Kaktoogwassees frowned. "If I seek no revenge I shall be deemed a coward by the members of my tribe. I can never be chief."

Marie pleaded with him, her words flowing from her heart, and in the end he gave in to her entreaties.

They decided not to wait until the occasion of *uik paltimk*, as custom demanded, but to be married in midsummer. The ceremony would be conducted according to the ancient rites of the Micmac tribe. If Marie was troubled that no Christian minister would bless their union, she gave no sign; but she wanted the ceremony to take place on the shores of Minnewauken, near the spot where Kaktoogwassees had dived into the spring to bring up the healing stone which had saved her life.

Before anything else could take place, however, the magic stone had to be returned to its resting place. After La Belle Marie's miraculous recovery the services of Masu were called upon again.

Another procession took place. Nine times the people walked around the magic circle, giving thanks to the spirit of Mineota. Reverently Kaktoogwassees entered the sacred ground and lifted high the medicine stone in praise and gratitude. But as he did so a cry of dismay came from the watching people. A fine red powder filtered through Kaktoogwassees' fingers as the stone crumbled to dust.

Now there was anger and fear among the people, and looks of hatred were directed at Kaktoogwassees. He had used the medicine stone to save the life of a paleface, and so it had been lost forever to the Micmac. Again the braves protested furiously that the marriage should not take place, for this was a warning from Glooscap that the son of a chief had no right to mix his blood with that of an alien. When it was evident that Kaktoogwassees was determined to have La Belle Marie as his wife, in spite of the anger of the Council, many braves left the camp. None of them would come to the wedding feast.

But there were some who remained loyal to Kaktoogwassees and some who had learned to love La Belle Marie. Preparations went forward. On a glorious day in July the wedding took place. Indian maidens had built a bower and decorated it with lovely woodland flowers. The bower stood in front of the chief's wigwam where the wedding ceremony was to be celebrated. Many people, French as well as Indian, came to witness the unusual marriage. Inside the wigwam the brief ceremony took place. The handsome young couple emerged, radiantly happy, to receive the blessings of the guests.

At that instant there came the twang of a bowstring. An arrow sped through the air and struck the breast of Kaktoogwassees. Marie's scream rang out across the waters of Minnewauken and echoed through the forest. She threw herself upon the prostrate form of her husband and tore at the arrow, but Kaktoogwassees died in her arms.

Dressed in her embroidered bridal costume of white leather, Marie could be seen wandering up and down over the sand dunes.

3

The Witch

La Belle Marie now avoided the company of the Indians. She knew it was a Micmac who had killed her mother and it was a Micmac who had killed her husband. Her heart was broken. She who had always loved people, who had danced and sung with such joyous and innocent abandon, now became a sad and solitary recluse. She lived in the log hut on the shore of La Grande Source. At times she left her abode and, dressed in her embroidered bridal costume of white leather, she travelled to the north shore where she could be seen wandering up and down over the sand dunes. Sometimes she sang, and so mournful and plaintive were her melodies that the fishermen put down their gear and stopped work to listen.

Sometimes in her loneliness Marie would come to where they were working. The fishermen would share a simple meal with her, and try to joke and tease her out of her melancholy. But there was never an answering smile. She would only gaze at them with dark eyes, eyes which had grown enormous in the pale oval of her face.

Several women of St. Peter's looked upon her with deep suspicion, and turned away quickly whenever they saw her walking along the path in the village.

The two Sulpician monks who had come with the first settlers had become so discouraged with their work that

in the spring of 1723 they had left their post and returned to France. They had complained to their supe-
riors of the difficulty not only of converting the Micmac
to Catholicism but also of preventing them from contin-
uing to practise their age-old pagan customs. Besides,
complained the monks, sorcery and witchcraft were still
practised among some of the fishermen and their families, especially amongst those who had come under the
influence of two evil women, Madame Grandville and
her daughter. These two women were heretics, claimed
the monks. Madame had attended Mass very irregu-
larly, and La Belle Marie seldom entered the Church.
Marie's father, who had been hanged as a pirate, was
known to have been a Protestant.

For some weeks during that fateful summer of 1723
there had been no priest at Port LaJoye; and then
a Franciscan monk, Father Louis Barbet Dulonjon,
came to the island from the new-founded monastery at
Louisbourg. He had been chosen to succeed Father
De Breslay. Father Dulonjon was a young and humble
follower of St. Francis, committed to a life of poverty and
abstinence. It was thought that he should be better able
than old Father De Breslay to endure the bitter hardship
of a place cut off from the outside world for six months
out of every year.

No sooner had Father Dulonjon arrived to take up his
duties than he was assailed with complaints about La
Belle Marie. The women of Port LaJoye believed the
unfortunate young woman had supernatural powers.
They accused her of walking the beaches in order to
seduce the fishermen from their tasks. Indeed, she had
so bewitched the men that they often asked her to go
with them upon the water, believing she could avert
storms and prevent accidents. When a wind arose and
the sea grew rough, Marie would sing a strange melody
in an unknown tongue. Then the waters would grow

calm. The sailors would be lulled to rest, and as they lay idly on their oars, there were those who vowed that they had seen the fish rise in great numbers to the surface and stay there motionless, as if charmed by the magic of her voice.

Some claimed her power was always for the good. If anyone was hurt or fell ill, they said, La Belle Marie offered healing salves and medicines. But even so, scoffed the women, it was known that her presence in any community was invariably followed by bad fortune. Certainly the Indians were not as friendly as they had been before Marie had come to Isle St. Jean. Worse, this young woman, soon after her mother's death and without showing any signs of grief, had married the son of a chief. And she had not been married in the Christian church, but according to the ancient rites of the savages.

Greatly alarmed by these tales, Father Dulonjon went at once to the hut at La Grande Source, and tried to examine La Belle Marie. But she only stared at him with her great tragic eyes and refused to respond to any questions. Convinced that the girl was indeed possessed by a demon and was a very dangerous influence on both the Indians and the fishermen, the priest reported to the Intendant at the fort, the man in charge of all civil and criminal offences.

La Belle Marie was arrested and thrown into prison on a charge of practising witchcraft. On the day of her trial many accusers testified to her guilt and not one of the persons she had befriended had the courage to speak in her defence. The beautiful girl who had once danced like a fairy to the tune of the fishermen's fiddles, and who had sung like a bird as she flitted along forest paths or wandered across sandy beaches, was found guilty and condemned to be burned at the stake for her sins.

"It is written in the Bible," said the Judge. "'Thou shalt not suffer a witch to live.'"

Marie would sing a strange melody in an unknown tongue.

Marie was dragged back down into the underground prison and there chained to a stone wall to await the day of her execution.

4

Medardus

At first Marie struggled against her bonds like any captured wild thing. She who loved light and laughter and who had lived long in the out-of-doors within the sound of the wind whispering in the pines and the waves of the ocean breaking upon the beaches was terrified of the dark and oppressive silence. Only when a meal of bread and water was thrust through the bars was she offered the brief, dim light of a tallow candle, and only then could she hear the sound of a human voice. She pleaded with her jailers, begging them to believe in her innocence and to break the chains and the iron bands which held her chafed and bleeding ankles. But they looked at her with fear and horror, and often hurried away without a word as soon as they had performed their duties.

Always the words of the Judge echoed and re-echoed in her head:

"On the morning of the 17th of November, in the year of our Lord 1723, you shall be taken to the hill called Point de la Flamme, and there, between the Black Cross and the Holy Church, you shall be tied to a stake and your body committed to the flames. May God have mercy on your soul."

In the pitch darkness day and night were alike. At last Marie sank into a stupor of despair, and she no longer asked, "What day is this?" when an attendant brought her food. But a time came when, as she lay huddled and shivering in a corner of her cell, footsteps approached which sounded unlike the quick, military tramp, tramp of a soldier. It was a soft, hesitant tread. Marie looked up to see the bright light of a torch and heard the rattle of a chain as someone unlocked the door of the cell.

"Who are you?" she cried, even as she recognized the long gown and shaven head of a young priest.

"I am Medardus," said the monk, in a gentle voice. "I have come to offer you the comfort of confession so that your soul may be saved from eternal perdition."

"Why, what day is this?" cried Marie, in terror.

"It is the evening of the 16th day of November."

Marie shrieked in anguish and threw herself face downwards, clawing at the cold, damp earth with her broken nails. Calmly Medardus fastened his torch in a ring that hung from the ceiling, and bent down to lift the tormented girl to her feet.

"Don't be afraid," he comforted.

She lifted her head. Their eyes met, and she saw pity and compassion in his, something she had not seen for a long time. Then his expression changed to one of startled wonder. She knew he was conscious of her physical beauty, and a great hope surged in her breast. She saw his eyes fill with tears which flowed down his cheeks, unheeded. She pulled herself to her knees, entwined his ankles with her arms, and gazed up into his face. She wept with him, and when at last she could speak, she whispered,

"How kind you are! You are the only one who has wept for me. Oh! As I love God, so I love you."

A look of shock and horror passed over the priest's face, and he tried to disentangle himself from her encircling arms.

"Be careful!" he warned. "This is no time for blas-

High and true her voice soared above the sound of the crackling flames.

phemy. Be mindful of the hour. Remember your fate! Your body must perish in flames, but by penance and prayer, even at this late hour, your immortal spirit can be saved."

"Of what shall I repent?" she sobbed. "I am innocent. I am no more a witch than you. Both my parents are dead...and my dear husband...all those who truly loved me have lost their lives through acts of violence. Now, I, too, must die. What is my sin?"

"Hush," said Medardus. "You know you have been guilty of singing obscene songs that have enchanted the hearts of men. Be assured that it is Satan himself who has possessed your body, and it is he who sings through you. Only confess, and your soul shall be saved from Evil."

La Belle Marie laughed through her tears.

"Do you not know that my mother was a Basque? It was she who taught me those songs, songs which are as old as the earth, as old as the stars in the sky. It is in the nature of our people to sing. We have a song for everything—for work and for play, for birth and for death. As I must breathe, so must I sing."

The young priest was deeply troubled. His whole body trembled as he tried to control himself. Marie rose to her feet and pressed her quivering lips against his face.

"Save me, Medardus!" she pleaded passionately. "Help me to escape! I know a way. Unbind these chains. There is an escape passage that leads from this prison to the beach. Come with me! You are young, and the blood flows swiftly in your veins. We can find happiness together. We shall run away and hide in the forest. I know where money and jewels are buried. We can escape from this awful place...."

Her voice faded, and then La Belle Marie began to sing. Her sweet pure voice rose in a joyful melody as she sang of a land of sunshine and flowers and singing

46

birds. The priest stood in a trance. Then Marie's lips sought his, and as he responded a great shudder passed through his body. He thrust her away from him.

"Temptress!" he cried. "What are you doing? Shall my soul, too, be condemned to everlasting Hell? God have mercy upon you!"

He rushed out of the cell and ran down the passage. Marie's song changed to a doleful dirge. He covered his ears as he ran to shut out the sound of her haunting voice.

The next morning at dawn, when the eastern sky was stained as red as blood behind the Black Cross and the Holy Church, La Belle Marie was led forth to her execution. Many people had gathered near the pyre, built on Point de la Flamme, to observe the burning of the witch. The tongues of the women were silent as they watched the young girl stand drooping, her head bowed, as she was tied to the stake.

Now the priest, Medardus, stepped forth alone, holding the holy crucifix. His step was faltering and unsteady. Marie lifted her head and met his eyes, which looked at her with such an agony of fear and despair and horror, that her own filled with compassion for him. Their gaze held as the executioner touched his flaming torch to the pyre, and suddenly Marie began to sing the same joyful sweet melody the priest had heard the night before. High and true her voice soared above the sound of the crackling flames.

To Medardus it was a song of love and forgiveness that would haunt him to the end of his days.

The End

Epilogue

Many, many years after Medardus watched Marie burn at the stake, he lay on his deathbed in France. The monks in his cloister heard a haunting melody coming from his cell. When the Father Confessor went to hear Medardus's final confession, he heard instead the story of "La Belle Marie."

Medardus, old and feeble, lay dying on his couch, singing the Basque melody Marie had sung as she burned. Then, suddenly, Medardus sat up, reached out his arms in a passionate gesture, and cried out:

"I hear you. I am ready for you, woman most true and guiltless. A witch they proclaimed you. I see your sweet body which basely they burned, your eyes of kindly affection, your graceful limbs in beauty welling. I see anew the heavenly bliss once tendering itself to me, which I, disdaining, gave over to death. After fifty years full of repentence and pains I come to abide eternally with you."

And so he died.

To this day, the story of Marie is told by the Micmac of Prince Edward Island. The bubbling source is thought by some to be in the western part of the Island, a place now called Scales' Pond. Some think it is near Fort Amherst or Rocky Point. Still others think the spring is, indeed, near St. Peter's. The clear water which bubbles up out of the earth at these places seems to echo the unearthly melody which haunted Medardus.